CARTOONS No. 22

from

Evening Standard

and

CHAPMANS
1990

Chapmans Publishers Ltd
141–143 Drury Lane
London WC2B 5TB

First published by Chapmans 1990

ISBN 1 85592 702 0

Printed and bound in Great Britain by
Clays Ltd, St Ives plc.

September 21, 1989

A Wiltshire vet was left £3 million in a 90-year-old spinster's will.

"Of course you don't need a doctor, m'lud, just keep taking the Bob Martin powder and worming pills six times a week!"

October 12, 1989

A cache of explosives was found on Hampstead Heath.

"Don't move a muscle! You could be lying on 50lbs of Semtex!"

October 13, 1989

A "have a go" girl working in the City foiled a robbery when she took on the thieves.

"You know, that girl's wasted in options!"

The dignity of the law
was looking badly
crumpled after The
Guildford Four, jailed
for a terrorist bombing
15 years earlier, were
declared innocent and
released.

"We run them in, we let
them out, we run them
in, we let them out, we
show them we're the
bold gendarmes . . . !"

October 20, 1989

A new play about the celebrated connoisseur of London low-life opened in London.

"It looks like Jeffrey Bernard can afford a new car now!"

October 22, 1989

Several members of the Surrey police force were suspended after the Guildford Four were released.

"Come out with your hands up, you're surrounded by what's left of the Surrey police force!"

October 23, 1989

There were howls of protest when Junior Education Minister Angela Rumbold held dinners in the House of Commons to raise money for Tory funds.

"I think it was that speech by Nicholas Ridley that did it!"

October 24, 1989

Police turned hundreds of would-be acid house partygoers away from motorway services.

"Would you call dinner with the Bishop an acid house party, dear?"

October 26, 1989

A huge policy row blew up between Chancellor Lawson and Sir Alan Walters, Mrs Thatcher's special economic adviser.

"Shouldn't we just wait for Maggie to sack him, Nigel?"

October 27, 1989

Yves St Laurent's new collection included some risque breast-baring designs.

"Have you forgotten something, Doris, or is that another exclusive creation by Yves St Laurent?"

October 31, 1989

Two unnamed Tory backbenchers were apparently ready to stand against a beleaguered Maggie in a leadership battle.

"Ah, Ponsonby! Guess whose name came up in our search for a man of burning ambition, courage and suicidal tendencies, to stand against Mrs Thatcher."

November 1, 1989

There was a new poisoned food scare when a supermarket chain had to withdraw tuna from its shelves.

"A friendly gesture from the management: Indonesian tuna sandwiches!"

November 8, 1989

Private Eye fought a series of libel actions and in one the award against them was drastically reduced by the Court of Appeal.

"And here's to the next long drawn-out libel case!"

November 12, 1989

Apart from providing the souvenir business with an instant product, how could the old wall be used . . . ?

"What else could we do with it!"

November 14, 1989

Germans celebrating the end of the Berlin wall had started removing pieces as souvenirs.

"That O'Reilly never misses a trick, does he!"

November 17, 1989

Police in Leeds were adopting disguises to help them trap prostitutes.

"It'll be a fiver as usual, officer!"

November 19, 1989

Labour MP Clare Short led a campaign against the sale of sex magazines in newsagents' shops.

"I said, we'd better keep that one under the counter too, just in case Clare Short happens by!"

November 22, 1989

A gang was prosecuted for stealing food and selling it when no longer fit for human consumption.

"Green sausages! It's what everybody's demanding these days, luv!"

November 24, 1989

For the first time in her 10 years as PM, someone had stepped forward to challenge Mrs Thatcher for the Tory leadership.

"The name of the man behind putting up Sir Anthony Meyer to oppose you is aaaaAAAAAAAAGH!"

November 27, 1989

The Sunday trading controversy continued, even though many people found open shops rather convenient.

"This bench will NOT tolerate Sunday shopping at B&Q!"

December 1, 1989

Sir Anthony Meyer was brave enough to challenge Mrs Thatcher for the Tory leadership.

"I daren't support you, Sir Anthony, but would there be a place for me in your cabinet?"

December 3, 1989

For the first time Fleet Street editors signed a code of practice issued by the Press Council to curb invasions of privacy.

"It's all right, vicar, you will get the right to reply!"

December 4, 1989

A storm-tossed shipboard summit meeting in Malta was delayed when rough seas prevented President Bush from reaching the talks.

"I hope we don't go on meeting like this!"

December 5, 1989

Courtaulds banned workers from drinking during working hours.

"Not the chairman! You fool, not the chairman!"

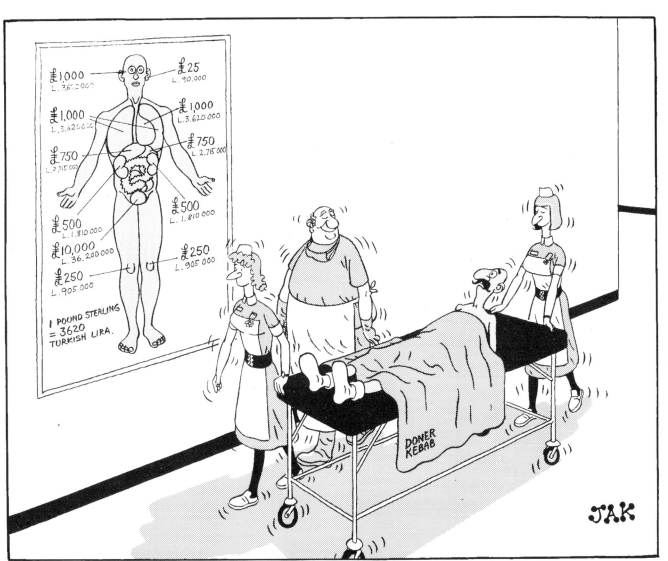

December 6, 1989

Three doctors faced disciplinary action after paying a Turk several thousand pounds to remove one of his kidneys for spare part surgery.

"I only came in for a job in the kitchens!"

December 7, 1989

Another food scare. This time certain micro-wave ovens were accused of not making food hot enough to kill off all bugs.

"I hate to complain, Mavis, but has this chicken been in the micro-wave long enough?"

December 8, 1989

A virulent form of 'flu was sweeping the country.

"Pity it's not a Wednesday, you could give it to Mrs Thatcher!"

December 11, 1989

It was World Cup draw time, and England's group stages were scheduled for Sardinia.

"I say, Reggie, remember you said the only drawback to your idyllic Sardinian retreat was that there were no English newspapers?"

December 12, 1989

Philomena Conneely, a 23 year old factory worker from Galway, won nearly £2 million in an Irish lottery.

" . . . and I'm Patrick Conneely, your fifth cousin twice removed, from Tipperary!"

December 13, 1989

British Rail was involved in a massive modernisation scheme, but would it be enough?

"I'm not saying my ministry is completely sold on the idea, but see how many you can stuff into a compartment!"

December 17, 1989

Christie's sale of car registration numbers raised £1.54 million.

"Well, if you didn't buy that Chippendale sideboard at Christie's, what did you spend the £100,000 on then?"

December 19, 1989

The Labour party was trying to change its image and some of its policies—but not with universal approval.

"If Kinnock gives up any more socialist aims, you won't be able to tell the difference between us and the Tories!"

January 4, 1990

Labour MP Ron Brown appeared in court charged with causing damage at his former mistress's home, and with stealing her knickers.

"Judging by the Janet Reger labels, I'd say we're on the trail of a Conservative!"

January 5, 1990

A heavily disguised Michael Caine appeared on TV in Jekyll and Hyde.

"Your usual table, Mr Caine?"

January 7, 1990

Glasgow was European City of Culture 1990. Would this change things?

"Hey, Jimmy! Can you spare a fiver for a wee drop of Chateau Latour '59?"

January 10, 1990

Cost estimates for the Channel Tunnel were soaring, leading to squabbles about who would have to stump up the extra money.

"Oh, look! They're going to do another estimate!"

January 11, 1990

A woman who bought some rabbit in a butcher's shop, discovered when she got home that it was in fact dog.

"Well, if you don't want rabbit, how about a nice chicken or duck?"

January 14, 1990

The perils of Bovine Spongiform Encephalopathy made eating beef a worrying affair.

"The doctor thinks it's hormone deficiency, the vet thinks it's mad cow disease."

January 16, 1990

Three men attempting to rob a Belfast betting shop had been shot dead by British soldiers.

"I'm coming out with my winnings, and I'm not wearing a mask!"

January 17, 1990

The army was criticised for the previous day's Belfast shooting. Labour MP Ron Brown wasn't being allowed to forget his recent court case involving stealing his mistress's knickers.

"Using the Labour party technique, you wave a pair of knickers at the masked gunmen, shouting in a loud, clear voice, "Freeze! Freeze! This is the British army!"

January 19, 1990

A top Scottish judge resigned over allegations that he was involved in a homosexual conspiracy involving young boys.

"Ladies and gentlemen of the jury, have you reached your verdict? Personally, I find him very attractive!"

January 25, 1990

Sunday Times editor Andrew Neil was suing the Sunday Telegraph and its former editor Peregrine Worsthorne over articles implying Mr Neil knew his former girlfriend Pamella Bordes was a prostitute during their affair.

"Hello, darling! Fancy a nice time?"

January 26, 1990

Fleet Street was enjoying the editors' embarrassment.

"Have you got any 'What the editor saw' machines, old boy?"

February 2, 1990

Princess Alexandra's pregnant daughter Marina Ogilvy finally agreed to marry in church to avoid any further embarrassment for the Royal Family.

" . . . and for another fiver you could have the corgis join you!"

February 4, 1990

Former Army press officer Colin Wallace claimed there had been a smear campaign against certain politicians and a cover-up of events in Northern Ireland during the Seventies.

"You're surrounded, O'Reilly—give yourself up or we'll send in the dirty tricks boys!"

February 7, 1990

WRENs were to be allowed to sail on Royal Navy ships for the first time.

"I am sorry, Miller, but you've picked the wrong time of the month to see the Captain!"

February 9, 1990

Colin Wallace continued his allegations about cover-ups in Ulster.

"I wish to bring to the House's notice a campaign of dirty tri. . .!"

February 11, 1990

Cruft's time, and dangerous dogs were still in the news.

"Look here, McTrusty, about these Rottweilers of yours."

February 12, 1990

For the first time in their history, the Boy Scouts were admitting girls to their ranks.

"We wanted Stanley to join the Boy Scouts, but his heart was set on the Brownies!"

A serious fire almost
destroyed the Savoy
Theatre, and caused 150
guests at the Savoy
Hotel to be evacuated
in the middle of the
night.

"I say, chef! Go easy on
the flambe!"

February 15, 1990

It was the beginning of what became known as the Guinness fraud trial, which was expected to last about six months.

"... and this has been earmarked for the lawyers' fees in the Guinness case!"

February 16, 1990

Several children were injured in a schoolyard after three rottweilers escaped from a nearby house.

"New regulations, madam. The dogs are all right, but we've got to put your husband down!"

February 17, 1990

Britain and Argentina re-established diplomatic relations for the first time since the Falklands War.

"Ah! Welcome back, Carlos, old boy—I believe you know these ladies?"

February 19, 1990

There was financial squabbling over who should finance what for the Channel Tunnel.

"D'you know, Wilson, I haven't seen a boardroom battle like that in years!"

February 20, 1990

Two thugs attacked
Leader of the House Sir
Bernard Braine after he
made an anti-abortion
speech.

"We were only trying to
help an old Tory MP
across the road!"

February 22, 1990

A bugging scandal erupted around two British firms involved in a bitter takeover battle after a listening device was found during a security sweep of an executive's office.

"Personally, I feel it an honour and a privilege to work for a chairman who's regarded as having the finest brain in British business today."

February 23, 1990

Radio 4's Today programme had been heavily criticised by Norman Tebbit for having a left-wing bias.

"After Tebbit called you a snivelling wet red queen why did you have to ruin it all by hitting him with your handbag?"

February 26, 1990

Ambulancemen were offered a pay rise which would add 13 per cent to the NHS wage bill, but many said it was still not enough.

"Sorry we're late, mate, we're only a 13 per cent ambulance!"

February 27, 1990

Dr David Owen announced he might not stand at the next general election. Did this mean he might resume his medical career?

"Sorry about that, Mr Simcock, but I'm a bit out of practice!"

February 28, 1990

Hackney Free School was slated as the worst school in the country.

"I ain't done bad for an old East Ender, 'ouse in the country, got me roller, and we've got young Wayne's name down for Hackney Comprehensive!"

March 1, 1990

Hurricanes and torrential rain had brought extensive flooding to some parts of the country.

"You'll love this one, it has its own trout stream!"

March 4, 1990

England's test cricketers amazed and delighted the country by beating the West Indies on their own home ground.

"The Bishop feels you've gone slightly over the top with our victory. Now, if we'd won three in a row . . . "

March 7, 1990

The greenhouse effect was blamed for aggravating the acne of millions of people.

"Well, I suggest some pills for the Majorcan acne, and a garden centre for the greenhouse effect!"

March 8, 1990

After concerns about rottweilers and pit bull terriers, what could possibly outscare the new "horror" dog, the Bandog?

"It's an Australian Crocweiler."

March 9, 1990

A damning report on the Fayed Brothers' takeover of Harrods said they had lied about their financial assets at the time of the deal.

"He's lying, deceitful and devious. He should be a huge success in the international takeover business!"

March 11, 1990

Mr Tiny Rowland's Lonrho company had been the prime mover in pushing for an investigation into the Fayed Brothers.

"It was horrible, Sir Edward. I was just taking dictation when a mummy rushed in and laid a curse on Mr Rowland!"

March 12, 1990

Throughout the country council meetings were violently disrupted by protestors as the members tried to set the level of the new poll tax.

"And finally, a two minute silence for Councillors Snodgrass, Wilkins and Smedley, who went down so gallantly during the anti poll tax protest!"

March 14, 1990

The effects of emergency repairs to the Victoria Line threatened to lead to months of chaos for London's commuters.

"I see old Bentley has managed to get a seat as usual!"

March 15, 1990

Two convicted Irish terrorists were freed by a court on a technicality.

"Have a nice day, lads. See you in court!"

March 16, 1990

A Tube disaster was narrowly avoided when a Piccadilly Line train was driven the wrong way down a tunnel.

"Excuse me, am I all right for the Piccadilly Line?"

March 20, 1990

Former racing driver Stirling Moss was injured when he was knocked off his moped.

"I've always wanted to say this—'Ello, 'ello, who do you think you are, Stirling Moss?"

March 21, 1990

BP was wielding the redundancy axe.

"What free gift would you like with your petrol, madam, an ex-refinery worker, an ex-motor mechanic or an ex-£100,000-a-year manager?"

March 22, 1990

A group of Belgian nuns decided to sell their valuable convent and enjoy a taste of the high life.

"My eyes aren't what they used to be; is that the Cardinal or the toy boy I ordered?"

March 23, 1990

Another Soviet state had chosen to regain its independence, and for the first time since glasnost and perestroika the Russian tanks were rolling.

"Slow down, Boris, I think we've just run over Lithuania!"

March 28, 1990

The Queen's nephew, Viscount Linley, was suing the Today newspaper for libel over a story that he was allegedly involved in a beer-throwing incident in a Chelsea Harbour pub.

"I don't care whose aunt you are, you're barred!"

March 30, 1990

A row blew up about Labour MP Chris Mullen, who claimed in a book to have tracked down the real villains behind the Birmingham pub bombings. A TV documentary was made about his investigations.

"I'm a Labour MP, and I must warn you that anything you say may be taken down and used in a book and a TV documentary against you!"

April 2, 1990

There was looting, violence and hundreds of arrests when an anti poll tax demonstration in Central London turned into the biggest act of civil disobedience for decades.

"You can't possibly drive home, George, look at the way you parked when you got here!"

April 3, 1990

After the poll tax riots in Central London the first cases were reaching court.

"Surely you remember me! I was dining in a charming little West End restaurant when YOU kicked the window in!"

April 4, 1990

A minor earthquake, centred on Wrexham, rattled homes all over the country.

"Did the earth move for you too, Gwyneth?"

April 5, 1990

The Duke of Edinburgh listened to an Old Bailey murder trial involving sex romps and adultery, after the Duke had made a traditional visit to dine with judges.

"Well, it wasn't quite like this!"

April 6, 1990

Two surgeons were disciplined for taking transplant organs from a Turkish patient without his knowledge or permission.

"What did old Abdulla sell to the transplant doctor this time, Fatima?"

April 8, 1990

Labour announced new alternatives to the poll tax, including a scheme basing charges on the cost of rebuilding a property.

"I know it'll save us from the poll tax, Brian, but I'm really going to miss my fitted kitchen."

April 9, 1990

Music was blared at rioting prisoners at Manchester's Strangeways jail.

IN DOLBY STEREO
Shirley Valentine

ELDORADO CHOC ICES · ICE CREAM

JAK

"Personally, I think you're getting too many concessions as it is!"

April 10, 1990

A list was published of the richest 200 people in Britain.

"The Duke of Westminster's only got two O-levels and look how much money he's got!"

April 11, 1990

Prince Edward told the Daily Mirror he was tired of people thinking he was gay.

"But, Edward, you don't have to prove yourself to me, I'm your mother!"

April 12, 1990

A Channel 4 programme skirted round the law preventing terrorist groups from speaking on TV by having actors synchronise their voices with Sinn Fein president Gerry Adams's words during an interview.

"First of all, let me say how grateful my friend is to Michael Grade and Channel 4 . . . !"

April 15, 1990

Greenpeace was campaigning against Britain becoming a dumping ground for toxic waste from other European countries.

"Of course it be nice round here. There be just six inches of soil between you and half a million tons of toxic waste!"

April 19, 1990

At their annual conferences, teachers were considering taking industrial action over pay, against union leaders' advice.

"Chalky White, a striking school teacher, you passed on Maths, History, English, Latin, French, Physics, Biology and Humanities!"

April 23, 1990

Baroness de Stempel was jailed for seven years for embezzling £500,000 from her aunt.

"Got you again, Watkins. I'd have you up before the Baroness if she wasn't doing seven years herself!"

April 24, 1990

A report on the filthy state of our hospitals was enough to make anyone feel ill.

"That's not creamed cod, luv, that's yesterday's Irish stew. They've forgotten to wash the plates again!"

April 26, 1990

The British-made Hubble telescope at first failed to operate when it was launched with an American space probe.

"All right! Which bloody idiot left the lens cap on?"

April 27, 1990

After 25 days the Strangeways prison siege was over, but not everyone was satisfied with the Governor's softly softly tactics.

"All right, Clever Dick! And how would you have got them down from the roof?"

April 29, 1990

A new film was released about the Kray twins' violent past as London gang bosses.

"It used to be so tough round here, the police had to walk in pairs!"

May 1, 1990

BSB, Britain's latest satellite broadcasting system, took to the air.

"It's terrible, we're getting Robin Day with Derek Jameson's voice!"

May 2, 1990

Prince Philip criticised the old maxim "Where there's muck there's brass", saying that these days there shouldn't be muck at all.

"I hope you haven't washed for a few days, Eric, we've a meeting with a big client today!"

May 3, 1990

Britain baked in some of the hottest weather on record, which was worrying the Tories on the day of municipal elections.

"Bloody weather! That could be our majority out there!"

May 4, 1990

American teacher
Frank Reed became the
second western hostage
in eight days to be freed
in the Lebanon.

"Ah, Rushdie, we've
been asked to make a
conciliatory gesture
towards Iran over the
hostages; I'm sure you'll
understand . . . !"

May 6, 1990

Britain's municipal elections had been a worrying time for the Tories, who did better than they had expected in some areas.

"I say, Pater! It's all right to lower the drawbridge—the Tories retained control of the council."

May 10, 1990

An audience at Covent Garden booed a performance of Il Trovatore after a singer's voice cracked.

"I must warn the audience that the police have the power to veto any high risk opera performance!"

May 11, 1990

Michael Heseltine re-entered the poll tax row by announcing an alternative plan which would mean much higher charges for higher rate taxpayers.

"... then Daddy had this wonderful idea to hit the rich ...!"

May 13, 1990

Organisers of the £90,000 Hennessy Ladies Cup in Paris admitted that several contestants were chosen for their looks rather than their golfing prowess.

"Let me assure you ladies that, unlike the Hennessy Cup tournament, none of you has been picked for her looks!"

May 15, 1990

The mad cow disease scare prompted several education authorities to take beef off the school dinner menus. A cat had caught it, so could it spread to humans?

"If you think the beef was mad, wait till you taste the cat!"

May 16, 1990

Speaker of the House of Commons Mr Bernard Weatherill told scruffily dressed MPs to smarten up, or risk not catching his eye during debates.

"I'd rather you went back to being scruffy, Dennis. People will think you're after my job!"

May 30, 1990

The IRA shot dead two Australians in Holland, thinking they were British soldiers.

" . . . and these I got for mistakes!"

The French banned British beef because of fears about mad cow disease.

"Of course it's not British beef, monsieur—Regardez le beret!"

June 3, 1990

A report branded Britain's beaches a disgrace after many failed pollution tests.

No, we haven't cleaned up this beach yet, but you get a jolly good dip when you come out."

June 4, 1990

Beef sales slumped because of fears about mad cow disease, and high interest rates depressed the housing market, driving some estate agents out of business.

"Of course, at one time you could have sold the place to an estate agent!"

June 5, 1990

The Lords threw out the War Crimes Bill, which would have allowed prosecutions to begin against surviving Nazi suspects in Britain.

"Ach! I know they can't prosecute you now, Otto, but they'll almost certainly throw you out of the British Legion!"

June 7, 1990

The picture of the Queen on the new £5 notes issued that day had been criticised for making her look too old and grumpy.

"No wonder she's looking cheesed off. What can you get for a fiver these days?"

June 8, 1990

The Guinness fraud trial heard that Ernest Saunders gave the go-ahead for the takeover of Distillers in an attempt to put the Guinness company on a par with the Rothschilds.

"Hello, Jacob! Have we got more money than Guinness?"

June 10, 1990

The start of the World Cup may have been good news for football fans, but most wives weren't quite so keen.

"Hello, dear, it's half time—any chance of a cup of tea?"

June 12, 1990

The captain of a British Airways BAC 1-11 jet was almost sucked out of his plane when part of the windscreen fell out at 23,000 ft over Oxfordshire. Crew members saved his life by hanging on to his legs.

"Who are we hanging on to up front?"

June 13, 1990

The Government refused to put any money towards the cost of a high speed rail link between London and the Channel Tunnel.

"Will the passengers from the French High Speed Train arriving from Paris transfer to the number 11 tram for King's Cross!"

June 15, 1990

Norman Tebbit criticised Lord Young for becoming the £350,000 a year head of Cable and Wireless "too soon" after having been Trade and Industry Secretary.

"I'm afraid the new chairman will be a little late. He hasn't resigned from the cabinet yet!"

June 17, 1990

The Government refused to fund a high speed rail link between the Channel Tunnel and London. Critics claimed the slower journey would damage Britain's trade.

"Look, Dad, it's one of those fast French trains."

June 19, 1990

Industrial espionage hit the headlines when car park giant NCP planted a spy with their rival company Europarks to discover their business secrets.

"Europarks have just got the contract for a car park in Milton Keynes, aaaggghh . . . !"

June 20, 1990

An order for 33 Tornado fighter bombers was cancelled after £600 million was lopped off the defence budget.

"It's the RAF practising for next year's fly past!"

June 22, 1990

Chancellor John Major announced plans for a new European currency unit (Ecu) to go into circulation at the same time as existing national currencies.

"Is there a 'k' in Ecu, Mr Powell?"

June 25, 1990

The first day of Wimbledon, and this year the competitors were younger than ever.

"No kids! She's the Number Three seed!"

June 27, 1990

The IRA blew up the Carlton Club in St James's injuring eight people.

"I do hope you're not going to come home from your club in that state every night!"

The World Cup authorities in Italy deported 247 England fans for hooliganism, although many claimed they were innocent bystanders.

"Mildred and I were just admiring those wonderful friezes on the gate of the Herculaneum when we were seized by the Carabinieri for some reason or other!"

July 3, 1990

Germany unified its currency, which brought new prosperity to the East.

"It's lovely, Hermann, but I thought you were going to buy a tractor with the Deutschmarks!"

July 5, 1990

Thirty million TV viewers watched England lose to Germany in the World Cup semi final.

"Where were you on the night of 4th July between 6.30 and 10.00pm?"

July 6, 1990

England football manager Bobby Robson had appeared in a Hamlet cigar advert after his team's World Cup defeat. Perhaps Mikhail Gorbachev, wilting under Russia's political problems, could do with a cigar too.

Happiness is a cigar called . . . !

July 26, 1990

There were searching inquiries into allegations that miners leader Arthur Scargill diverted money sent to miners during their 1984 strike.

"Would that be the Sean O'Scargill, Seamus O'Scargill, Liam O'Scargill or Paddy O'Scargill account?"